PANCHATANTRA

The stories of *Panchatantra,* originally written in Sanskrit, are very old. Legend has it that a king who had three foolish sons engaged a versatile teacher, Vishnusarman who taught them how to be happy and successful in life. *Pancha* means five, *tantra* means doctrines of conduct or modes of action, namely, confidence or firmness of mind, creation of prosperity or affluence, earnest endeavour, friendship, and knowledge.

Panchatantra depicts *nitishastra* (wise conduct of life) through stories, mainly of animals, which children love to read.

Contents

The Monkey And The Crocodile

A MONKEY lived on a rose-apple tree by the side of a river. The rose-apple tree had plenty of fruits all the year round. There is nothing a monkey likes better than rose-apples. One day a crocodlle came out of the river and went close to the rose-apple tree.

"Who are you?" shouted the monkey from the tree-top.

The crocodile looked up, saw the monkey and said, "I am a crocodile from a place far away. I am just wandering in search of food."

"Food? I have plenty of rose-apples here. Try one. If you like it, I can give you as many as you want." So saying, the monkey plucked a few rose-apples and threw them down. The crocodile ate them and said, "I like them very much. This is the best fruit I have eaten in all my life."

The monkey threw down more rose-apples and the crocodile ate them all. The crocodile asked,

"Can I come again? Will you give me some more fruits?"

"You are always welcome," said the monkey. "You are my guest; you can eat as many rose-apples as you want."

The crocodile said he would come again and took leave of the monkey.

Next day the crocodile came back. The monkey was happy to see him and gave him more rose-apples to eat. The monkey and the crocodile became friends.

Every day the crocodile visited the monkey. They spent much time together. They talked about everything they knew. One day they talked about their families and friends. The monkey said he was alone and was lucky to have a friend like the crocodile. The crocodile said he lived with his wife on the other side of the river.

"You have a wife?" said the monkey. "You did not tell me that before. I would have given you rose-apples for her also."

The crocodile said he would love to take some to his wife. The monkey plucked many rose-apples and gave them to the crocodile. The crocodile went home with the monkey's gift. His wife liked the rose-apples very much. She wanted to have more of them and her husband said he would try to get her some every day.

The monkey and the crocodile became close friends and spent more and more time together. When they parted in the evenings, the monkey

always gave the crocodile a gift of rose-apples for his wife.

The crocodile's wife loved rose-apples, but she did not like her husband coming home late every day. She wanted to put a stop to it. She said one day, "I feel you have been telling me a lie. How can you, a crocodile, spend so much time in the company of a monkey? He is not of our kind. We kill monkeys and eat them."

"I am telling you the truth," said the crocodile. "This monkey is a friend of mine. He likes me and I like him. He lives on the rose-apple tree and

I visit him every day. He gives me rose-apples to eat and even sends some for you."

'If the monkey eats only these sweet rose-apples,' thought the crocodile's wife, 'his flesh must be sweet, too. A most delicious dinner he would make if only I could get him here.' Then she said aloud, "If you are really his friend, why don't you invite him home one day? I would very much like to meet him."

"No, no, I don't think I can do that," said the crocodile. "He lives on land and may drown if he tries to swim across."

"But you are his friend," said the crocodile's wife. "You just invite him. A monkey is always clever. He is sure to find a way to come here."

The crocodile was not happy about inviting his friend home. With every passing day, his wife's craving for the monkey's flesh increased. She had to find a way to get at the monkey and she thought of a plan.

One day she pretended to be very ill. She shed tears as though she was in great pain. The crocodile was sad that his wife was ill. He sat by her side and said, "What can I do to help you?"

"I am very ill," said his wife. "I asked the doctor and he said I would get well only if I ate a monkey's heart."

"A monkey's heart?"

"Yes, dear, a monkey's heart. You must get your friend's heart if you want me to get well."

"How can I do that? He is my only friend and I cannot think of doing him any harm."

"Then go and live with your friend. You don't love your wife. You love only your friend. You want to see me dead. Then you can be with him always."

The crocodile was unhappy. He could not think of doing his friend any harm. At the same time he could not let his wife die.

"How can I kill my friend?" he asked, shedding tears.

"What is your difficulty in killing a monkey? Crocodiles have to kill other animals if they are to live."

The crocodile shed more tears; he did not know what to do.

"You don't love me," said his wife. "I have decided to end my life. When you come back today, you will find me dead."

The crocodile began to think. As a husband it was his duty to look after his wife. He decided to save her life. So he went to the rose-apple tree.

When the monkey saw him he asked, “Why, my friend, why are you so late? Did you meet with an accident on the way?”

“No accident,” said the crocodile. “My wife and I had a quarrel. She said I am not your friend. You have done so much for us, but I have not yet invited you home. Now she is eager to meet you and has asked me to take you home today.”

“How sweet of her to ask me home,” said the monkey. “I too would like to meet her. But how can I get there? You live in water and I would drown if I tried to go to your place.”

“We live on the river bank,” said the crocodile. “I can take you there easily. You can ride on my back while I swim.”

The monkey thought it was a good idea. He was happy he had good friends like the crocodile.

With the monkey sitting on his back, the crocodile swam across the river. On reaching the middle of the river, the crocodile began to sink.

"Hey," cried the frightened monkey, "what are you doing? I shall drown if you go down any further."

"I am going down further," said the crocodile. "I want to kill you."

"Kill me? Why?" asked the monkey in surprise. "Why, my friend, why do you want to kill me?"

"My wife is ill and the doctor has said she must eat the heart of a monkey to get well. You are the only monkey I know. I have to kill you and give your heart to her."

The monkey was shocked. He knew his life was in danger. What could he do? He thought hard for a while and said, "My good friend, why didn't you tell me before? I would be most happy to give my heart to save your wife. But how can I do it now? I keep my heart safe in a hole on the rose-apple tree. I have not brought it along. If you had told me what you wanted before we set out, I would have gladly given you my heart then and there."

"Is that so?" asked the crocodile.

"Yes," said the monkey, "let us go back at once and get the heart before your wife gets worse."

The crocodile turned back and swam as fast as he could to the rose-apple tree. When they got there, the monkey jumped off and hurried up the tree. Perched comfortably on a high branch, he looked down at the crocodile and said, "Now you can go back alone to your wicked wife and tell her that her husband is the biggest fool in the world."

The Big Lion And The Little Rabbit

ONCE THERE lived a huge lion in a vast jungle. All the other animals were afraid of him, because every day he hunted and killed them in large numbers. Before long, they knew, none of them would be left alive. They had to find a way to stop this senseless killing.

One day they met and decided to go to the lion himself.

Next day a large number of animals went to the lion.

He roared in happiness, for he thought he could kill them all without having to hunt for them.

"Your Majesty," said their spokesman, "please hear us before you try to kill us. You are our king and we are your subjects. The rate at which you are killing animals, none of us will be left in the jungle except you. How can there be a king without subjects? When we all die, you will no longer be a king. We want Your Majesty to remain our king forever. We have, therefore, a humble suggestion. We ask you, Great Lord, to stay at home always. We, on our part, will send you one animal every day for your food. Your Majesty will not have to hunt anymore and will have enough food at home. Thus the king and his subjects can live in peace."

The lion thought over the matter. He felt there was some sense in what the animals proposed.

"All right," said the lion. "I agree to your plan. But, if you fail to send me my food on any day, I will kill as many animals as I like."

The animals promised they would not let him down.

From that day, every day, one animal went to the lion to be eaten up. This went on for a long time. One day the turn of the rabbits came. A little rabbit was asked to go to the lion. This rabbit was very clever. He did not like the idea of being killed and eaten by the lion. There must be a way to save himself and, if possible, the lives of other animals also.

He thought for a long time and at last decided on a plan.

The rabbit set out for the lion's den. But he was in no hurry. He took his own time.

The lion was very hungry by the time the rabbit arrived, and he was furious when he saw a puny little animal coming towards him. He roared, "Who sent you here? You are too small for a meal and you are very late. I shall teach all the animals a lesson for sending you here. I will kill them all."

The little rabbit bowed low and said, "O, Great King, please hear me. You will not blame me or other animals for what has happened. They all knew that one rabbit was too little for you and so had sent six rabbits. On the way, five of us were killed and eaten up by another lion."

"Another lion?" roared the lion. "Who is he? Where did you see him?"

"He is a big lion," said the rabbit. "He came out of a big cave. He was going to kill me also, but I said to him, 'You don't know what you have done. We were all going to our king. Now you have spoiled his dinner. He is not the sort of king who will allow such things to happen. He will come and eat you up. Be prepared!'

"He then asked me, 'Who is this king of yours?'

"Our king is the biggest lion in this jungle," I said. He was furious and said, 'You know, I am the only king in this jungle and all the animals here are my subjects. I can deal with them as I like. This fellow you say is your king is an imposter. Bring him here and I shall show him who the real king is.' And he sent me to take you there."

On hearing this, the lion roared and roared in anger and his roar shook the whole jungle.

"Show me the way to the place where this fool lives," said the lion in fury. "I cannot have peace until I see him and kill him."

"Quite so, Master," said the rabbit. "The fellow deserves to be killed. How I wish I were bigger, for then I myself would have torn him to pieces."

"Show me the way," said the lion, "show me the way."

"Yes, Master, please come with me." The little rabbit led the lion to a well in the jungle.

"There, My Lord," said the rabbit, "he stays in

this fortress. Be careful, an enemy in a fortress is difficult to deal with."

"Leave that to me," said the lion. "Where is he?"

"He was right here when I saw him," said the rabbit. "The moment he saw you coming, he might have jumped into his fortress. Come, Sir, I shall show him to you."

The rabbit went to the well and asked the lion to look down. The lion looked into the well and saw his own image reflected in the water.

He roared in anger. From inside the well came a louder roar. The lion heard the echo of his own voice and thought it was the roar of the other lion. He did not wait a second longer.

Into the well jumped the lion to kill the enemy. His head crashed against the rocks. He fell into the water and was drowned.

The little rabbit returned home and told the other animals how he had got rid of the dreaded lion.

The Stork And The Crab

ONCE UPON a time there lived a stork by the side of a tank. There were plenty of fish in the tank and the stork had enough to eat. Years passed. The stork grew old and weak. He found it difficult to catch all the fish he wanted for his food. At times he had to go without food. He feared he would die of starvation.

The stork thought of a plan. He stood by the side of the tank, looking sad. He did not even try to catch the fish which went past him. The fish, frogs and crabs in the tank noticed how sad the stork looked and wondered what had happened to him. A big crab went up to him and asked, "Why do you look so sad? Why are you not taking your food?"

The stork replied, "I have spent all my life by the side of this tank. I have always been happy. Now things are going to change. All the fish in the tank will soon die and I shall be left without food."

"Why, Uncle?" asked the crab.

"Because I heard people say that they will soon fill this tank with earth and grow crops over it. Then there will not be any fish left alive."

The fish, crabs and frogs in the tank heard what the stork said. They were alarmed. So they went to the stork and said, "Uncle, you have given us bad news. However, you are wise. Please tell us how we can avert this danger."

The stork said, "I am only a bird. Even so, I may be able to help you in a small way. There is a bigger and deeper tank some distance away.

It cannot be filled up so easily. If you want, I can take you all there."

"You are our only friend, Uncle," said the fish. "You can save us. Please take us to that tank."

"It is difficult," said the stork. "But I shall do my best."

"Take me first, take me first," cried every fish in the tank.

"Have patience, please," said the stork. "I can carry only a few at a time. But I shall try to make as many trips as possible. You must know that I am old now and I would need a little rest after every trip."

Soon the stork set out on his first trip. He took a few fish in his beak and flew away. He did not, however, take them to another tank as he had promised, but carried them to a big rock and there he ate them up. Then he returned to the tank. He took a few more fish, only to fly with them to the rock and make a meal of them. Having had

enough food for the time being, he rested for a while. When he felt hungry again, he went back to the tank to pick up some more fish.

He came to the tank as often as he felt hungry.

Still left in the tank was the big crab. He felt he should also leave the place and save himself. So he said to the stork, "Uncle, save me also."

The stork was getting tired of eating fish and he thought he might try a crab for a change.

"Of course, my young friend," said the stork, "I am here to help you. Come, I shall take you to the big tank."

The crab was happy when the stork picked him up and flew away. After a while, the crab looked down. He wanted to see the tank he was going to live in, but he could not see any water anywhere. Soon the stork was flying down.

"Uncle, where is the big tank you are taking me to?"

"Ha, ha, ha," laughed the stork. "Don't you see the huge rock down there? That is the place I am taking you to. That is the place I took all the fish to."

The crab could now see the rock clearly. There were heaps of fish bones on the rock. He was frightened. He knew the stork would land on the rock, kill him and eat him, as he had done with all the fish.

The crab thought hard. Suddenly he dug his sharp claws into the stork's neck. The stork struggled, flapped his wings and tried his best to get rid of the crab. The latter was pressing the bird's neck with all his strength. Soon the stork fell to the ground. The crab cut the head off the stork's body and dragged it to the tank in which he lived.

His friends in the tank were surprised to see him back. "Why, brother?" they asked. "Why have you come back? What happened to Uncle Stork?"

"Here he is," said the crab, "only his head." He then told them how the stork had been cheating them and how the lie had put an end to him.

The Crows And The Black Snake

FATHER CROW and Mother Crow had their nest in a huge banyan tree. They had been living there for a number of years and had many children.

One day a large black snake came and made its home in a hole beneath the banyan tree. The crows did not want a snake as their neighbour. Yet they could not do anything about it.

Mother Crow laid eggs and soon they were hatched. Father Crow and Mother Crow brought up their children with great care.

One day the crows went out in search of food. The snake crawled up the tree and ate the young crows. When Father Crow and Mother Crow returned, they were shocked to find their little ones gone. They did not know what had happened to them. They asked all the birds and the animals in the neighbourhood; nobody could tell them how their children had disappeared.

They cried for a long time and decided to keep a better watch when they had children again.

Months passed. Mother Crow laid eggs and soon they had baby crows. This time the crows kept a more careful watch over the children. One of them always remained at home while the other went out to get food.

One day Mother Crow saw the snake coming up the tree. She cried for help and tried her best to drive it away. She could not succeed. The snake crept up and ate the baby crows.

Mother Crow cried and cried. Many other crows joined her and all of them cried and tried to attack the snake. The snake went into its hole before the crows could harm him.

The crows were still crying when Father Crow returned. He was very sad when he heard of the fate of the little crows. He tried to console Mother Crow who was heartbroken. Between sobs she said, "We must leave this place immediately. So long as the black snake lives here, we are not safe. We shall go far, far away and make our home somewhere else."

Father Crow was unhappy. "We have been staying here for many years. It will be sad indeed to leave our home."

"If so," said Mother Crow, "who will protect us from this wicked black snake?"

Father Crow replied, "We will have to find some way to drive away the snake. We have our friend, the old fox. He is intelligent. Let us consult him."

Mother Crow agreed. They went to the fox and told him everything. "Help us!" they cried. "Save us from the snake or we will have to leave our home and go away."

The old fox thought for a while and then said, "You need not leave your home. You have been staying there for many years. We have to find a way to get rid of this snake. I think I can help you. Do as I tell you and there is every chance that the snake will be killed. Now, listen to me. Tomorrow morning the ladies of the royal palace will go to the river for their bath. They will keep their ornaments and clothes on the river bank before they enter the water. Their servants will be there, at a distance, keeping a watch over the valuables.

"You should go there and find out where they keep their ornaments. When nobody is near, one

of you pick up a necklace or any other valuable ornament and fly away. You must cry aloud so that the servants will see you flying away with the ornament. They will run after you to get it back. You must fly straight to the banyan tree and drop the ornament into the snake's hole."

The crows agreed to do what the fox had told them. Next morning, they went to the riverside and waited. The ladies of the royal palace came and left their ornaments and clothes on the bank before they went into the river, exactly as the fox had said they would. The crows looked at the ornaments. They noticed a pearl necklace among them. Mother Crow flew down, picked up the necklace and flew away. Father Crow followed her, cawing loudly all the way.

The servants saw the crow taking the necklace and ran after her. The crows went straight to the hole where the black snake lived and Mother Crow dropped the necklace into it.

The servants tried to take it out with a long stick. The snake was disturbed and came out hissing and raised its hood. The servants surrounded the snake and beat it to death. They took out the necklace and went away.

Father Crow and Mother Crow were happy the snake was dead. They were grateful to the old fox.

The Musical Donkey

ONCE A washerman had a donkey. The donkey was old and lean. During the day the donkey had to carry heavy loads of clothes; at night he was free to go about.

The donkey happened to meet a jackal. They became friends and wandered together in search of food.

One night they found a garden full of ripe cucumber. They went in and ate as much as they could. The next night they went there again and ate as much cucumber as they wanted. Thus night after night they visited the garden and had a dinner of ripe cucumber. Soon the donkey became fat. A few days later the donkey felt so happy after eating the cucumber that he said to the jackal, "Look, Dear Nephew, the moon is shining in the sky, the night is pleasant, and I feel like singing."

"Don't, Uncle, please don't," said the jackal. "It will only bring trouble for us. The farmers will hear you and come after us. We are thieves here. It's better to keep quiet."

"Dear Nephew," said the donkey, "everything here is lovely and I feel so happy that I must sing a nice song."

"No, Uncle," said the jackal, "better not. Besides, your voice is not very pleasant."

"You are jealous," said the donkey. "You have no taste for music."

"Very true, Uncle," said the jackal. "However, your music is sweet only to you. If you sing, the farmers will hear you and their reward you may not like. So you better not sing."

"You are a fool, a big fool. Do you think I cannot sing sweet songs? Now listen to me..." So saying, the donkey lifted his head to bray.

"Very well, Uncle," said the jackal. "You can sing as much as you like; I shall wait for you outside the garden."

The donkey began to 'sing'. The farmers heard his loud braying. They knew that a donkey was in the garden and they all rushed there with weapons. The donkey was still braying when they started beating him. They beat him so hard that the donkey fell down. The farmers tied a heavy mortar round his neck before they left.

The jackal was waiting outside the garden when the donkey dragged himself out with the heavy mortar.

"Dear Uncle," said the Jackal, "so the farmers gave you a big reward for your singing. Congratulations!"

"I am sorry, Nephew," said the donkey, "that I did not listen to you."

The Tortoise And The Geese

ONCE THERE was a tortoise in a large tank. He had two geese as friends. The geese used to come to the tank and the three of them spent much of their time together. They lived happily for many years.

Then there was a drought in the country; for a long time there was no rain. Rivers and tanks were drying up. There was famine in the land. People and animals were dying. Birds were flying away to places of safety.

The two geese saw danger from the drought. They decided to go away to another place. They met the tortoise to take leave of him.

"Why do you bid me farewell?" said the tortoise. "Am I not your friend? Why do you leave me here to die?"

"How can we help you?" asked the geese. "We can get to any place on earth by flying. You can't travel like that."

"It is true that I cannot fly like you," said the tortoise, "still, you can help me and take me with you."

"How can we do that?"

"That is easy," said the tortoise. "Bring me a stick. I can hold the middle of the stick with my teeth. Both of you take hold of the ends of the stick with your beaks and fly up, taking me along. Fly slowly to a place where we will be safe from this drought."

The geese thought over the matter and said, "We hope we can manage this, but there is one danger in the plan. If, by chance, you attempt to speak a word while we are up in the air, you will lose your hold on the stick, fall down and be crushed to death."

"I will do no such foolish thing," said the tortoise. "I will not utter a word as long as we are in the air."

So all of them agreed to the plan. The geese brought a strong stick and held it with their beaks at both ends. The tortoise held on to the middle of the stick with his teeth. The geese flew up, carrying the tortoise with them. They flew higher and higher. They flew over fields and hills and then they flew over a city. The people of the city noticed the strange sight in the sky. They had never seen anything like that before. They clapped their hands and shouted, "Look! How wonderful! Two birds carrying a tortoise, and see how they are doing it."

The tortoise did not like the people shouting and said, "Why should these fools shout like that?"

Even as he uttered the words, he lost hold of the stick and down he went. When he hit the ground he was killed.

The Ass Has No Brains

THE LION, the King of the Forest, had grown old. He could no longer run fast. He could not hunt. Often he had to go without food. As time passed, he grew weaker and weaker. He knew he could not go on like this. Somehow he had to get enough food, otherwise he would die. How was he to get his food? He thought and thought. At last he decided he should have an assistant.

The lion could not think of anybody other than the fox. So he called the fox and said, "My dear friend, I have always liked you, for you are wise and clever. I want you to become my minister and advise me on all affairs of the state."

The fox would not trust the lion. He was sure there was a catch in the offer. However, he could not say 'no' to the king. "Your Majesty," he said, "I feel honoured. I shall do my best to serve you. I accept your offer. Now tell me what I should do."

The old lion was pleased. He said, "I shall now tell you what your duties will be. You know I am the King of the Forest. A king must not run after other animals for his food. So your first duty will be to provide me with enough food. You will have to bring me one animal every day. I know you can do that without any difficulty."

"I shall do my best, Your Majesty," said the fox, and he went out in search of food for the lion.

On the way he met a fat ass. He said, "My dear friend, where have you been all these days? I have been searching for you for the last seventeen days."

"Why?" asked the ass. "I have been here all the time. Why did you want to see me?"

"To give you the great news," said the fox. "You are very lucky. Great honour awaits you. Our great king, the lion, has chosen you to be his Chief Minister. It was he who asked me to meet you and inform you of his decision."

"The lion?" said the ass. "I am afraid of him. He might kill me and eat me up. Why has he chosen me as his Chief Minister? I am not fit enough to be a minister. Please leave me alone."

The fox laughed and said, "You do not know your unique qualities, and that is your special charm. Our king has heard a great deal about you. He is dying to meet you. He likes you very much because you are wise, gentle, and hardworking."

The poor ass thought that perhaps what the fox said was true. He felt that he could trust the fox and go with him to meet lion. "All right," said the ass, "if you insist, I shall go with you to meet the lion."

"You are indeed wise," said the fox. "You must not lose your finest chance in life. Now, let us go and see our great king. His Majesty has told me many times all sorts of nice things about you. How happy he will be to meet you!"

Even as they approached the lion, the ass felt very frightened and refused to go ahead. The fox then said to the lion, "Your Majesty, the Chief Minister appears to be very shy and is hesitating to come near you."

"I like such modesty," said the lion. "I shall go to him myself." And the lion went limping towards the ass. At the sight of the lion, the ass was so frightened that he ran for his life.

When the lion lost his meal, he roared in anger

and shouted at the fox. You have played a trick on me. I was so hungry that I wanted to eat him up at once. Go and bring that ass back. If you don't, I shall kill you."

"Your Majesty," said the fox, "you were in too great a hurry. You should have left it to me to bring him near enough. I shall try again."

The fox went out and met the ass. "You are a funny fellow," said the fox. "Why did you run away like that?"

"I was too scared," said the ass. "I thought the lion was going to kill me."

"What a fool you are!" said the fox. "If the king

wanted to kill you, he would have done so. You could not have escaped by running away. The fact is, the king wanted to tell you a secret about the kingdom and he did not want me to hear it. Now what will our king think of you? Anyway, come back with me and ask for his pardon. You do not realize that by serving the king you will be the most powerful animal, second only to the king. All the other animals will respect you and seek favours from you."

The ass again thought the fox had told him the truth and so he agreed to go back to the lion.

The fox and the ass approached the Lion. Though Lion was now hungrier than ever, this time he did not appear to be in a hurry. He smiled and said, "Welcome, my good friend! It was unkind of you to have run away like that. Come, come nearer. You are my Chief Minister."

When the ass went closer, the lion pounced on him and killed him with a heavy blow on the head.

He thanked the fox for his cleverness. He was glad that at last he had some food to eat.

"Your Majesty," said the fox, when the lion was about to begin eating, "it is true that you are very hungry and it is time for your dinner, but the king must take a bath before his meal."

The lion thought the fox was right. "Very well," he said, "I shall go and bathe. You keep a watch on the ass.

The fox looked at the body of the ass lying before: him. He was very hungry. He said to himself,

'I took all the trouble of getting the ass here. And Lion almost lost him by his foolishness. It is I who deserve the best part of the meat.' Then the fox cut open the ass's head and ate up all the brain.

Lion returned and looked at the animal he had killed. It did not look quite the same. He found that the ass's head had been cut open. He asked the fox, "Who came here? What happened to the ass's head?"

The fox pretended to be very hurt. "Your Majesty, you still do not trust your most obedient servant. I have watched over the ass's body and I am sure nobody has touched it. Why, you yourself smashed the head of the poor ass when you killed him."

The lion was satisfied and began to eat. But suddenly, he shouted, “What happened to the ass’s brain? I wanted to eat the brain first.”

The fox smiled and said, “Your Majesty, asses have no brains. If this one had any, he would not have come here a second time.”

The lion saw the point.

The Girl Who Married A Snake

IN A little village far, far away, there lived a Brahmin and his wife. They were sad because they had no children. Daily they prayed and offered sacrifices to God so that they might be blessed with a child. At last the woman had a baby. The child turned out to be a snake! The couple was shocked and all their friends and relatives advised them to get rid of the snake as quickly as possible. Yet the woman refused to listen to them. The snake was her son and she loved him very much.

The woman looked after the snake with love and care. Every day, she bathed him carefully and fed him with the best food she could get. She made a cosy bed in a beautiful box and let him sleep on it.

The snake grew up. His mother loved him more and more. When there was a wedding in the neighbourhood, she began to think of getting her son married, too. But how could she find a bride for a snake? However, she did not give up hope. She thought and thought, wondering how to get a girl to marry her son.

One day, when the Brahmin came home, he found his wife in tears. “Why, what has happened?” he asked. “Why are you crying?”

She did not reply but continued to cry.

“Tell me,” said the Brahmin, “what is it that hurts you so much?”

However, she went on crying. The Brahmin stood helplessly beside her, not knowing what to do.

“I know you do not like me or my son,” she said at last. “You are not taking any interest in our boy. He is now grown up. You do not even think of getting him a bride.”

“A bride for our son?” asked the Brahmin. “Do you think anyone will give a girl in marriage to a snake?”

The woman did not answer but cried and cried so much that the Brahmin decided to set out in search of a bride for his son.

The Brahmin travelled far and wide but he could not find any girl who was willing to marry a snake. At last, he came to a big city where one of his best friends lived. The Brahmin had not seen him for a long time, so he decided to look him up. The Brahmin's friend was very happy to see him and they spent much time together. When it was time for the Brahmin to leave, the friend happened to ask him why he was travelling round the country.

"I am looking for a bride for my son," replied the Brahmin.

"Why did you not tell me this before?" said his friend.

"Now you do not have to go any further. I have

a daughter and she is beautiful. Here and now I give my daughter in marriage to your son."

The Brahmin was surprised and said, "I think it will be much better if you saw my son before you decide."

"No, no," said the friend, "it is not necessary at all. I know you and I know your wife, and that settles the matter. Let us not waste anymore time. My daughter will go with you. Marry her to your son."

The Brahmin's wife was happy. Here was a beautiful girl to marry her son. She started making preparations for the wedding. When the people of the village heard about it, they went to the girl and advised her not to marry a snake. The girl refused to listen to them.

"My father promised the Brahmin that I would wed his son," she said. "And I, his daughter, will never do anything against his wishes. If the Brahmin's son is a snake, then a snake I shall marry."

The next day, the marriage between the snake and the girl took place. The girl began to live with her husband. She was devoted to him and did everything for him like a good wife. And the snake still slept in his box.

One night, as the girl was going to bed, she saw a handsome youth in the room. She did not know who he was. She was very frightened and wanted to run away.

But the young man said, "Do not run away, my dear. I am your husband. Don't you know me?"

The girl did not believe him. So, to prove to her that he was really the one she had married, the man entered the snake's skin. Then he came out of it once more as the young man.

When she saw this, the girl was so happy that she fell at his feet.

At night, after everyone had gone to bed, the young man would come out of the snake's skin and stay with the girl till daybreak, Then, he would go back. This went on for quite a long time.

One night, the Brahmin heard voices coming from his son's room. He kept a watch. He saw the snake turning into a handsome young man!

The Brahmin at once rushed into the room, seized the snake skin and threw it into a fire, where it was burnt to ashes.

"Thank you very much, dear father," said the young man. "Because of a curse, I had to remain a snake until somebody, without my asking, destroyed my earlier form. Today you have done it, and I am now free from the curse."

And the young man never became a snake again.

The Mice That Ate Iron

ONCE THERE was a rich merchant called Naduk. As time went by, his business became so bad that he not only lost money but got into debt.

Naduk was unhappy. It was no use staying in the city any longer, so he decided to go on a long journey to try his luck elsewhere. He had to sell almost everything he had in order to pay off his debts. All that he was left with, which was of some value, was a heavy iron beam.

Before leaving, Naduk went to see his good friend, Lakshman. He was sorry to hear of Naduk's misfortune and unhappy that he was going away. "Is there anything I can do for you, my friend?" he asked.

"Well," replied Naduk, "I have a very heavy iron beam which I would like to leave with you. Will you keep it for me till I return?"

"Is that all?" said Lakshman. "No doubt, I will

keep it for you. You can be sure the beam will be quite safe with me. I shall give it back to you whenever you want it."

Naduk thanked his friend and went home. A few days later, he left the city.

Many years passed. Naduk went far and wide, carrying on his trade. He was lucky, for he did good business and soon became rich again. He then returned to his hometown with plenty of money. He bought a new house and started his business in a big way.

After some time, he went to visit his friend Lakshman. Lakshman was glad to see Naduk and welcomed him warmly. They talked of Naduk's travels abroad and his business. Later, as he was about to leave, Naduk said, "Now that I am here, may I have my iron beam back?"

Lakshman looked very worried. He had no intention of returning the beam because he knew it would fetch a good price if he were to sell it. So he said, “I don’t know how to tell you this. Something bad has happened. I put the beam safely in my store room, but now I find that mice have eaten it. I am really very sorry. Beams of that kind are difficult to get or I would have bought another for you.”

“Please don’t feel bad about it,” said Naduk. “It was not your fault that the mice ate up my beam. This just goes to show that nothing lasts forever.”

As he was leaving he said, “By the way, Lakshman, I have a present for you which I bought during my travels. Will you ask your son, Ramu, to come home with me? I will send it back with him.”

Lakshman felt very guilty. Not only had he got away with his lie but Naduk seemed to believe him. At the same time he was anxious to see what his friend had got for him. So, he called Ramu and asked him to go along with Naduk.

Naduk took the boy home. He led him to the cellar of his house, locked him in, and went about his work.

When Ramu did not retum home by evening, his father got worried. He went to Naduk and asked him where the boy was.

“Something terrible happened when we were on our way here,” replied Naduk. “A hawk swooped down and carried him off before I could do anything.”

"That is a lie!" shouted Lakshman. "How can a bird carry off a fifteen-year-old boy?"

A quarrel started between Naduk and Lakshman. A big crowd gathered as the two men shouted at each other. Finally, they decided to go to court.

As soon as they entered the magistrate's room, Lakshman cried, "Your Honour, this man has stolen my son. Please ask him to give me back my boy."

The magistrate ordered Naduk to do so.

Naduk said, "Sir, how can I when before my very eyes a hawk carried off the boy? What could I do?"

"You are a liar," shouted the magistrate. "How can a bird fly off with a boy?"

To this Naduk replied, "If the mice at Lakshman's place can eat up an iron beam, then a hawk can carry off a boy!"

The magistrate wanted to know what it was all about. Naduk related the whole story. The people in the courtroom had a good laugh. The magistrate then ordered Lakshman to return the iron beam to Naduk, and Naduk to return Lakshman's son.

Union Is Strength

ONCE A flock of doves flew far away from their home in search of food. Though they flew for miles and miles, they could not find anything to eat. Tired and hungry, they were flying over a forest.

The smallest of the doves was so tired that he said to the dove king, "O, King, please can we rest a bit?"

"Oh, come, little one, be brave," replied the king. "We are sure to find some food soon."

So the little dove flapped his wings harder. He flew so fast that he found himself ahead of all the others. Soon he turned to them and said, "Come on, hurry up, I can see some food down there."

The doves looked down, and there they saw, just below a big banyan tree, some rice scattered on the ground.

"Come, my friends," said the dove king, "let us eat."

Together the doves landed under the banyan tree and began to eat the rice.

Suddenly, a vast net fell over them. The doves were trapped in it.

"We are caught," cried the king. "What shall we do now?"

The next moment they saw a big, fat hunter coming towards them. He was carrying a huge club.

"We must do something immediately," said the dove king, "before the hunter kills us."

All the doves were struggling to get out of the net. "How can we save ourselves?" they cried. "Tell us what to do."

"I have an idea," said the king. "We must act together. We shall all fly up, carrying the net with us. Remember now, unity is our only hope."

Each dove picked up the net with his beak. Then, all together, they flew up. The hunter was almost upon them when suddenly he saw his net going up into the air. He was amazed at the unity of

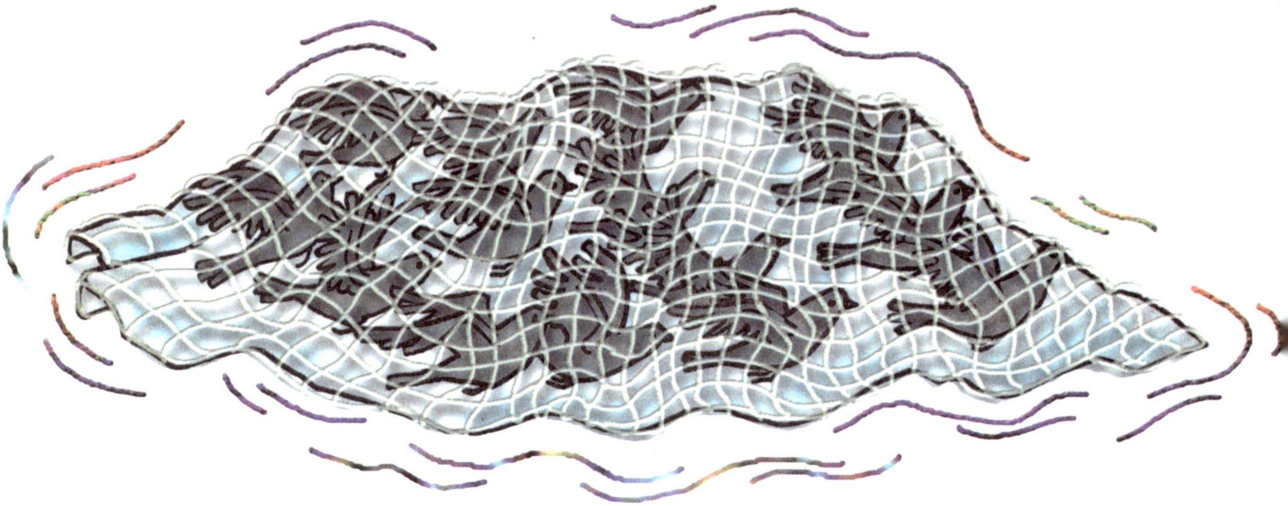

the doves in their effort to get away. He ran after them, hoping that the net and all the doves would soon fall down. The doves saw him running after them. So they flew high over hills and dales and went far, far away where the hunter could not follow them. At last, the hunter grew tired and gave up the chase.

When the dove king saw that the hunter no longer followed them he said, "Half our troubles are over. Now we must fly to the hill near the city of temples. There lives my faithful friend, a little mouse. He will certainly help us. He will cut the net with his teeth and set us free."

"Yes, yes, let us go to the city of temples," said all the doves in chorus and on they flew. Soon they reached the place where the mouse lived.

When the mouse heard the loud noise made by the flapping of wings, he was frightened and hid himself at the far end of his house. But the dove king called to him softly and said he had come to ask for his help.

The mouse looked out. He was happy to see that it was his friend, the dove king, who was talking to him.

"We have been caught in a trap set by a hunter," said the dove king. "We cannot get out of this net. When the hunter came, we flew together taking the net with us. Now please help us. Cut the net with your teeth and set us free."

"Very well," said the little mouse and he began to bite through the net. "I shall set you free first."

"No, no," said the king. "Please free my followers first."

The little mouse was wise. He understood the feelings of a king towards his subjects. So, he began to cut the rest of the net. One by one, all the doves were set free. And then, at last, the dove king was also set free.

All the doves were grateful to the little mouse for saving them. With a loud flapping of wings, they rose in the air and flew away.

The Brahmin's Dream

LONG, LONG ago there lived a poor Brahmin, who had to beg for a living. Sometimes, he had to go without food for many days. Often he had barely a handful to eat. But, one day, he got a potful of flour. He was very happy. He took the pot home and hung it up near his bed. Then he lay down on the bed and gazed lovingly at his pot of flour.

'I wish I were rich,' thought the Brahmin. 'Then I need not beg from door to door.' And the man began to dream.

'There is plenty of flour in that pot,' he said to himself, 'and it will last me for some days. Shall I keep it? Or shall I sell it? Suppose there was a famine in the land, I could sell it for a very good price. I would go to the market and callout, "Who will buy my flour?"

'And many people will come forward.

'"I will buy it for ten rupees," a man will say.

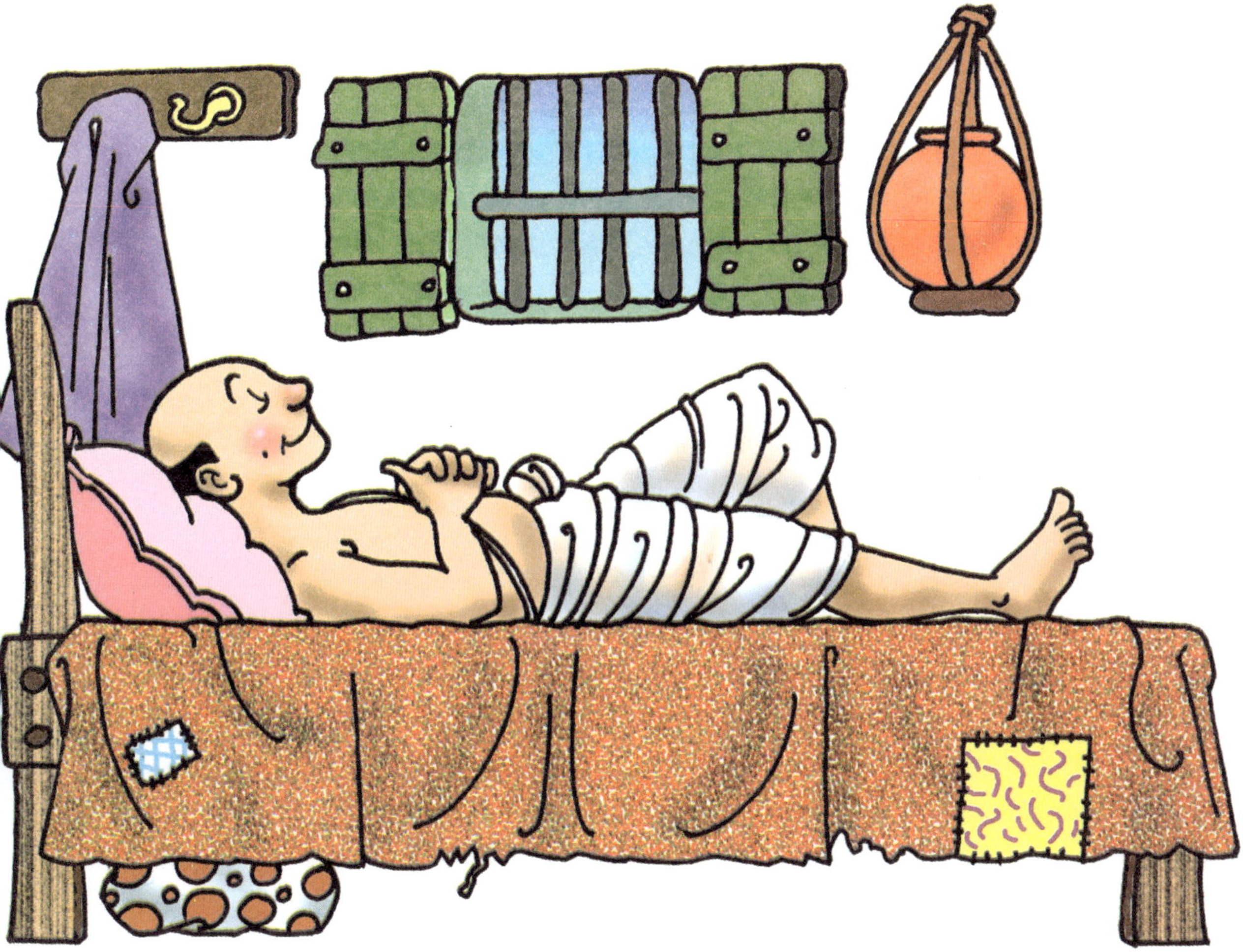

'"Here is fifteen," another will shout.

'"I will buy it for twenty rupees," a third man will say, and I shall sell him the flour for twenty rupees.

'Now, what shall I do with my twenty rupees? Shall I buy a pair of shoes and a dhoti? No, no, I shall not buy any of those. With my twenty rupees, I shall buy a pair of she-goats. Then I shall feed the goats on green grass and leaves. Soon the goats will have little ones and, in a few years, I shall have at least ten goats. Now, what shall I do with those ten goats? I shall sell them in the market. "Goats, goats, who will buy my plump goats?" I shall shout in the market.

'"Just the thing I was looking for," a villager with a red turban and a blue shirt will say, and he will buy my goats for one hundred rupees. Yes, for one hundred rupees!

'Now, what shall I do with those hundred rupees? Shall I buy a red silk coat? Or shall I buy a beautiful bed? No, no, I shall not waste my hundred rupees like that. I shall buy two cows. The cows will have calves, and the calves will grow up and become cows, and then all the cows will have more calves. And there will be lots and lots of milk. And I shall sell milk and butter and cream. And I shall make *burfi rasagulla* and *gulabjamun.* And have a shop of my own, with sweets piled up. "Sweets, sweets, who will buy my sweets?" I shall call out. "Who will buy my fresh sweets? Juicy sweets, sweets, sweets!"

'And along will come children with silver coins in their hands, and their mouths watering. And there will be men and women too, waiting for their turn to buy my sweets.

'And I shall do good business and I shall get richer and richer.

'Now, what shall I do with all the money I get? Shall I buy an elephant? Or shall I build a temple? No, no. I know what I shall do. I shall trade in pearls and diamonds. Yes, I shall buy pearls, diamonds and many other precious stones.

'Then I shall put on a lovely blue coat and a bright red turban and go to the king.

'"Pearls, diamonds, rubies, all for Your Majesty," I shall say. "Pearls, diamonds, all the very best."

'"Aha!" the king will say. "Just what I want for my queen."

'And I shall do more and more trade in pearls and diamonds and other precious stones. And I shall become a very rich man.

'Then I shall build a large house with beautiful lawns and mango groves. And there will be rare roses in my garden and pools full of red and blue and yellow and white lotus flowers. And white swans will be swimming about.

'Then many rich men will come to me and ask me to marry their daughters. Shall I marry one of those girls? Oh, no! Along will come the king himself and he will ask me to marry his daughter. Yes, then the beautiful princess with her long hair and lovely eyes will be my bride.

'And soon we shall have a son, and another, and then a daughter. And I shall play with my children in the garden. When I feel tired, I shall ask my wife to play with the children while I go and

take rest. My wife will be busy doing other things and the children will follow me. I shall not permit the children to disturb me when I am resting. I shall shout at them to go away. But children will be children. As they become more and more troublesome, I will get angry. I will pick up a stick and beat them, and beat them, and beat them!'

Imagining he was beating the children, the Brahmin began to beat the air with his hands. Suddenly, one hand struck against the pot of flour. Crash! The pot fell down and was smashed into a hundred pieces. The flour was scattered all over the floor.

"What was that noise?" said the Brahmin, jumping out of the bed.

He looked around him, but could see no princess, no big house, no lovely garden, no mango groves and, of course, no children! Only the broken pot and the flour spilled all over the sandy floor!

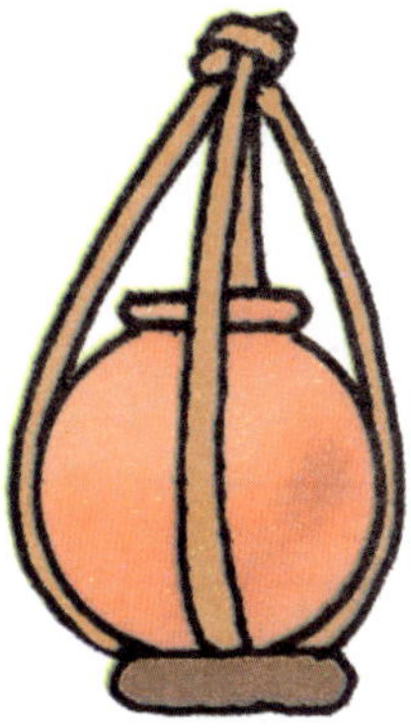

The Lion-Makers

LONG, LONG ago, there lived four friends. They were fond of each other and spent much of their time together. Three of them were very learned. They knew so much that they thought there was nothing more to learn. But, for all their learning, they lacked common sense. The fourth friend, on the other hand, was not at all keen to learn, but had a good deal of common sense.

One day, the four friends discussed how they could use their learning to earn money and better themselves. One of the learned men said they should travel far and wide, see the world and meet people of different countries. During their travels, they might win the favour of kings and nobles, and thus amass great wealth. All of them agreed it was a very good idea. The learned man added, "We three have studied everything and we are sure to do well during our travels. However, what about this ignorant fellow? He does not know anything. He will be a burden on us."

The second learned man replied, "Let him stay back."

The third said, "That is not the way to treat a friend. It is true he has not learnt anything, nevertheless, he has been our friend from childhood. We must not leave him behind."

So the four friends set out on a long journey. Soon they were passing through a dense forest. There they found, lying on the ground, the bones of a dead animal.

One of the friends said, "Here is a chance to test our knowledge. These are the remains of a dead animal. Let us bring it back to life."

The first learned man said, "I know how to put the bones together."

The second said, "I will take care of the skin, flesh and blood."

The third said, "I can bring the animal back to life."

So the first one assembled the bones; the second provided the skin, flesh and blood. The third was about to bring the animal back to life when the fourth shouted, "Stop! It is a lion! Don't bring it back to life!"

"You are a fool," cried the third learned man. "What do you know about these things? Do you think I can't bring a lion back to life? I can, and I shall!"

"Please wait a minute," said the ignorant fellow and he climbed up a tall tree.

The learned man brought the lion back to life. It was a huge lion. It stood up and looked at the three men. With a mighty roar he pounced on them and killed them. When the lion left, the 'fool' climbed down the tree and went home.

The Jackal Who Killed No Elephants

ONCE UPON a time, a lion and a lioness lived together in a forest. One day, two little cubs were born to them. The lion and the lioness were both very happy.

The lion said to the lioness, "You must stay at home and look after the babies until they grow up. I shall go out and bring you all the food you need."

Every day, the lion went hunting and brought home enough food. One day, however, he could find no animal to kill. In the evening, as he was

returning home, he found a baby jackal. He picked it up and took it to the lioness.

"This little jackal is the only food I could find for you today," said the lion. "Kill him and eat him. I could not kill him because he is only a baby."

"My dear," replied the lioness, "how do you think I can kill him? I am the mother of two babies just like him. No, I shall do him no harm. He shall be my third son."

So the lioness looked after the baby jackal. He lived with her two cubs and the three babies grew up together.

They ran about and played together and chased any wild animals they saw.

One day, a wild elephant came into the forest. The lion cubs followed him. They wanted to kill the elephant. But their brother, the young jackal, was frightened.

"Don't go near him," cried the jackal, "he is an elephant and he will kill you!" And the jackal ran away.

When they saw their brother running away, the lion cubs lost courage and ran home.

The lion cubs told their mother and father about the elephant and how their brother had run away. The young jackal heard this. He felt very hurt. He was angry and began to shout at the young lions. He told them he was not a coward; he was as brave as they were.

"Come out and fight with me, if you dare," he said.

The lioness took the young jackal aside. "You should not talk like that to your brothers," she said.

This only made the jackal angrier.

"What right have they to make fun of me?" he said. "Am I not as brave as they are? I will show them my strength. I will kill them both!"

The lioness only smiled at the jackal.

"You are brave," she said, "and you are also handsome, and you have brains. In spite of these, you see, jackals do not kill elephants."

"What do you mean?" he asked.

"Listen to me, my boy," replied the lioness. "Your mother was a jackal. I took pity on you. I brought you up like one of my own children. My sons do not know that you are a jackal. Now you should

run away and live with your own people. If you don't, my children will kill you and eat you up."

The young jackal was frightened. He quickly ran away.

Mouse-Maid Made Mouse

ON THE banks of the Ganga, there lived a large number of holy men. Their leader was a man of great learning. He also had magical powers and could do wonderful things.

One day, as he was saying his prayers after bathing in the Ganga, a tiny mouse fell into his hands from the beak of a hawk flying above. The holy man looked at the mouse. It was a lovely little she-mouse with a curly tail and shining black eyes. He liked her so much that he wanted to keep her. So, using his magical powers, he changed the mouse into a little girl.

He took the girl home to his wife.

"You have always wanted a child," he said. "Here is our daughter. Bring her up with love and care."

The holy man's wife was very happy that at last she had a daughter to care for. She said she would do everything for the child and bring her up like a princess.

Years passed and the girl grew up to be very beautiful. The holy man and his wife thought the time had come to find a suitable husband for their daughter.

"Our daughter should marry someone who is greater than anyone else," said the holy man.

"I think the Sun would be the best choice."

His wife agreed.

The holy man, using his magical powers, asked the Sun to come down. And the Sun came down.

"O, holy man, why did you call me?" asked the Sun.

"I want you to marry my daughter," the holy man replied. "She is very beautiful and very good. She is just the bride for you."

Mouse-maid was standing there; before the Sun could say anything she said, "No, no, father. I cannot marry him. I will burn with his heat. I want someone better."

The holy man felt sad. "Is there anyone greater than you?" he asked the Sun.

"Yes, there is," said the Sun. "There is the Cloud. When he covers my face, I cannot shine."

The holy man now called upon the Cloud to come down. And the Cloud came down.

"O, holy man, why did you call me?" asked the Cloud.

Before the holy man could answer, Mouse-maid said, "I will not marry him. He looks so dull and dark. Give me someone better."

The holy man asked the Cloud, "Is there anyone greater than you?"

"Yes, the Wind is greater than I am," said the Cloud. The Wind drives me about wherever he likes."

The holy man called upon the Wind to come down. And the Wind came down.

"O holy man, why did you call me?" asked the Wind.

"I want you to marry my daughter," said the holy man.

Mouse-maid said aloud, "No, no, father, I shall not marry him. He is always running about and cannot stand still for a moment."

"Is there anyone greater than you?" said the holy man to the Wind.

"Yes, the Mountain is greater than I," said the Wind. "He is so strong and tall that I cannot move him. I cannot even pass over his head."

The holy man called upon the Mountain to come down. And the Mountain came down.

"O, holy man, why did you call me?" asked the Mountain.

Mouse-maid again stepped forward and said, "No, no, father, he is too tall and rough and hard. I won't have him. I want someone better."

"Is there anyone greater than you?" said the holy man to the Mountain.

"Yes, the Mouse is greater than I am," replied the Mountain. "It is true that I am hard, and I am very strong. Yet the Mouse makes holes in me."

The holy man then called upon the Mouse to come. And the Mouse came.

The moment Mouse-maid saw him, she jumped with joy. "Father!" she cried. "He is the one I want. I shall marry him and love him with all my heart.

The holy man thought for a moment. Thereafter, using his magical powers, he changed the girl into a mouse and gave her in marriage to the Mouse.

The Loyal Mongoose

ONCE THERE was a farmer who lived with his wife at the far end of a village. They had a little son and they loved him very much. One evening, when the farmer returned home from work, he brought with him a little mongoose. He told his wife that this little mongoose would grow up and be a pet for their son.

The baby and the mongoose both grew quickly. In five or six months the mongoose was fully grown, while the farmer's son was still a baby. The mongoose became a lovely animal. He had two shining black eyes and a long bushy tail.

One day, the farmer's wife wanted to go to the market. She fed her son and put him to sleep in his little cradle. Then she took her basket and was ready to go.

Before leaving she told her husband, "I am going to the market. You must keep an eye on the baby. I do not like leaving him alone with the mongoose."

"Please don't be afraid," said the farmer. "Our pet is as sweet and loving as our baby."

The farmer's wife went to the market. The farmer having nothing to do, went out for a walk. He met some friends on the way and so did not return home for some time.

His wife came back with a basketful of groceries. She found the mongoose sitting outside as if waiting for her. As soon as he saw her, he ran to welcome her. The farmer's wife took one look at the mongoose and screamed.

"Blood!" she cried.

Indeed, the face and paws of the mongoose were red with blood.

"You have killed my son!" cried the woman.

And with all her strength she struck the mongoose with her heavy basket. She then ran straight to the child's cradle. She found the baby fast asleep. On the floor, below the cradle, lay a black snake, torn and bleeding.

The farmer's wife realized what had happened. She ran out looking for the mongoose.

"You killed the snake!" she cried. "You saved my child."

The mongoose lay still. He could not hear her. The basket had hit him on the head. The farmer's wife was sad she had acted so hastily. With tears in her eyes, she bent down and looked at the mongoose. He was dead.

The Ungrateful Man

LONG, LONG ago there was a poor Brahmin. He could not find enough work to do. Sometimes he and his family had to go without food. At last the Brahmin decided to leave his village in search of work.

Early next morning, before his wife and children woke up, he left the house. He did not know where to go or what to do. He just walked away.

He walked the whole day, until he came to a thick jungle. He was tired, thirsty and hungry. While looking around for water to drink, he found a well. He went to the well and looked in. There he saw a tiger, a monkey, a snake, and a man. They had all fallen into the well.

"O, noble Brahmin," the tiger called out to him, "please help me come out so that I can go back to my family."

"You are a tiger," said the Brahmin. "I am afraid of you. How can I pull you out of this well?

How do I know you will not kill me?"

"Don't be afraid of me, my dear man," replied the tiger. "I promise I will not do you any harm. Please take pity on me and save my life."

'I suppose I might as well save him,' thought the Brahmin. 'It is always good to be kind to others.'

The Brahmin reached into the well and pulled out the tiger.

The tiger thanked him and said, "Do you see those mountains over there? I live there in a cave.

I shall be happy if you visit me some day. Perhaps I could repay my debt to you."

The Brahmin then heard the monkey calling out to him from the well. "Holy Sir, won't you pull me out, too?"

The Brahmin at once pulled the monkey out.

The monkey thanked the Brahmin. "If you are ever in need of food, please call on me. I can give you as much fruit as you want. My house is over there, just below that big mountain."

Next, the snake called out to him. "Please help me, too."

"Help you?" exclaimed the Brahmin. "You are a snake. What if you bite me?"

"I shall never bite you," said the snake. "You need not be afraid of me at all. Please save me."

So the Brahmin pulled the snake out of the well.

"If you are ever in any difficulty," said the snake, "just call me. Wherever you are, I shall come to help you."

The tiger, the monkey, and the snake took leave of the Brahmin. But before they left, they spoke to him about the man in the well.

"Please do not help him," said one.

"If you do," said another, "you will be in trouble yourself."

As soon as they left, the man in the well began to call out. He begged the Brahmin to save him, too. The Brahmin felt sorry for the man and pulled him out too.

"Thank you for your kindness," said the man. "I am a poor goldsmith. I live in the city near here. If ever you need my help, please come to me."

The man went his way.

After some time, the Brahmin, too, continued his journey.

Now it so happened that luck was against him and he could find no work. In the end he thought it would be better to end his misery.

He made up his mind to jump into the river. Then he remembered the tiger, the monkey, the snake, and the man. He thought he would give them a chance to help him.

He went first to the monkey. The monkey was happy to see him. He gave him a warm welcome and offered him many kinds of fruits. There were mangoes, pineapples, grapes, and pomegranates.

"You are always welcome here," said the monkey

when the Brahmin told him how grateful he was.

Now the Brahmin wanted to see how the tiger would treat him. The monkey showed him the way to the tiger's home. As soon as the tiger saw the Brahmin coming, he ran out to welcome him. He had not forgotten the man who saved his life.

The tiger gave the Brahmin a gold necklace and other ornaments. The Brahmin thanked the tiger for his gift and went on his way.

His journey had at last brought him luck, he thought. He would be able to sell the ornaments for a good price. Then he could return home.

How happy his wife would be. With the money he would get, they could live happily. But who could help him to sell the ornaments?

He remembered the goldsmith. Would he help? He went to him. The goldsmith was glad to see the Brahmin.

"What brings you here?" he asked.

"I have come to ask for your help," replied the Brahmin.

"Here are some ornaments. Please help me to sell them."

The goldsmith took the ornaments and looked at them carefully. "I shall certainly help you," he said. "But let me show them to another goldsmith. Kindly wait here. I shall be back soon."

The goldsmith called his wife and asked her to look after the Brahmin. The goldsmith then went out and ran straight to the palace.

"Your Majesty," he said, showing the ornaments, "a man brought these to me and asked me to sell them. They are the ornaments I made for the prince. So I told this man to wait in my house and ran here at once, Your Majesty, to show them to you."

"Who is this man? Where is he?" roared the king. ""The prince was robbed while travelling through the jungle some months ago. I am sure fellow must have taken his ornaments."

"He is a Brahmin," answered the goldsmith, "and he is there, in my house."

The king shouted for his soldiers and they came running to him.

"Arrest the Brahmin who is in the goldsmith's house," ordered the king, and throw him into prison. Tomorrow we shall decide what to do with him."

The king's men seized the Brahmin and put him in jail. The Brahmin could not understand what was happening.

"Why have I been put in prison?" he asked the guard.

"Because you robbed the young prince and stole his ornaments," replied the guard. "You will certainly be put to death for this great crime."

The Brahmin was aghast. But what could he do? There was no one to help him.

Then he remembered the words of the snake he had pulled out of the well. So he called out to the snake. Soon the snake was by his side.

"What can I do for you?" the snake asked.

"Oh, please help me," cried the Brahmin. "I have been thrown into prison, and I am going to be killed for something I have not done." The Brahmin then told the snake what had happened. The snake thought for a while.

"I have a plan," said the snake. "I know how to save you. "

"Tell me," cried the Brahmin.

"I shall creep into the queen's room and bite her," said the snake. She will faint. No matter what they do, she will stay unconscious."

"What will happen?" asked the Brahmin.

"The poison will remain in her body until you place your hand on her forehead," explained the snake.

He left the Brahmin and went to the palace. He crept into the queen's room and bit her. The queen fainted.

The sad news that the queen had been bitten by a snake spread all over the land.

Doctors came from far and near, however, their medicines were of no use. No one could revive the queen.

Finally, the king declared that anyone who could cure her would be given a handsome reward. He sent his men to every town and village in the country. They walked through the streets beating drums and telling the people about the king's reward.

Many people went to the palace and tried to cure the queen, but all of them failed.

"I can cure the queen," the Brahmin said to the guards.

At once they took him to the palace and the king took him to the queen. There she lay in bed, looking more dead than alive. The snake's poison had turned her blue.

The Brahmin walked up to the queen and placed his hand on her forehead. Soon, she opened her eyes and sat up. The poison had left her.

There was joy throughout the land. The king was happy. He was grateful to the Brahmin.

"Your Majesty," said the Brahmin. "I was sent to prison for a crime I did not commit."

"What do you mean?" cried the king.

The Brahmin told the king the whole story, all that had happened from the day he left home until he was thrown into prison.

The king was angry when he heard what the

goldsmith had done. He at once had the goldsmith arrested.

The king was sorry the Brahmin had been put into prison for something he had not done. He, therefore, presented him with a large house and a thousand pieces of gold.

The Brahmin sent for his wife and children and they all lived happily.

The Cat's Judgement

A PARTRIDGE lived in her nest beneath a large peepul tree. She had been living there for many years. She was kind and friendly to all the little animals and birds.

One day, the partridge left her cosy home to look for food. She travelled far and came to a field of corn. It was time for the harvest, for the corn was fully ripe. The partridge was fond of ripe corn.

She remained in the field eating as much corn as she could. She made friends with the other birds there. She did not return home that day, or the next day, or the next. She stayed in the corn field for many days.

While the partridge was away, a rabbit found her empty nest. The rabbit had no home of his own, so he went to live in the partridge's nest and made it his home. When the partridge returned, she found the rabbit in her nest.

She was angry.

"What are you doing here?" she asked. "This is my house."

"Your house?" said the rabbit. "It is mine now. I have been living here for many days."

"You cannot stay here," said the partridge. "I built this house and I have always lived here. You can ask the neighbours."

"Why should I ask anybody?" replied the rabbit. "I found nobody living in this house, so I moved in. A house belongs to the one who lives in it. So it is my house now. You can ask the neighbours if that is true or not."

"No, it is my house," cried the partridge. "I went away for a few days to find some food. Now I have come back. Will you please get out of my house?"

"No, I won't." The rabbit was firm. "Here I am and here I stay."

The quarrel between the partridge and the rabbit went on for a long time. Many animals and birds gathered around. They heard what the partridge said, and they heard what the rabbit said. Nevertheless none of them could say to whom the house belonged.

They thought the partridge and the rabbit should find out what the law said. So they decided to take the dispute to a judge.

It was not easy to find a good judge. The rabbit and the partridge walked miles and miles, looking for a judge.

At last they came to the banks of the River Ganga. And there, at a distance, they saw a big Tom-cat.

They stood still. They were afraid to go further because they knew how dangerous a Tom-cat could be.

He was a wicked cat. He quickly closed his eyes and stood on his hind legs. Holding up a string of prayer beads, he prayed at the top of his voice.

The partridge and the rabbit were puzzled. They were seeing a holy cat for the first time. How well he said his prayers!

"I think we can ask this cat to judge our dispute," said the rabbit.

"Yes, I think so, too," said the partridge. "Still, we must be careful. A cat is our natural enemy."

They stood in silence until the cat had finished saying his prayers. The cat opened his eyes and looked at them.

"O, holy sir," said the partridge, "a little quarrel has arisen between this rabbit and me. It is about an important matter of law. Please decide it for us. You may punish whoever you find is in the wrong."

"Dear friend," replied the cat, "do not say such a wicked thing. You know I cannot bear to see others in pain. Yet you say I should punish one of you. Those who harm others will be punished by God. Now, do tell me what your quarrel is about. Then I will decide who is right and who is wrong."

"Well, this is what happened," said the partridge. "I went away for a few days and, when I returned, I found this rabbit had moved into my house."

"My house, my house!" shouted the rabbit.

"Now, please keep calm," said the cat, "and let me hear the whole story."

So the partridge told her story again, and when she had finished, the rabbit gave his story.

The cat sat in silence for a few moments. Then he spoke.

"I am very old," he said, "and I cannot see or hear you well. I have not quite understood your case. Won't you both come a little closer and tell me all about it again?"

The partridge and the rabbit were no longer afraid of the cat. They trusted him. So they both moved closer to him.

Before they knew what was happening, the cat had hit them hard with his paws. Both the partridge and the rabbit were killed and the cat ate them up.

The Four Friends

BY A lake in a forest, there once lived four friends. One of them was a small brown Mouse. He had big black eyes and a long tail. He lived in a snug hole near the edge of the water.

The second friend was a jet black Crow. He lived on a jamun tree close by.

The third was a Tortoise. He lived in the lake and was happy.

And the fourth was a Deer. She had beautiful large eyes, and her golden coat had many white spots.

The four were very happy together. They lived peacefully and no one troubled them.

One evening, Mouse, Crow, and Tortoise met beside the lake. They were waiting for their friend, Deer. They waited for a long time. But Deer did not come.

"What could have happened?" asked Mouse, worried.

"Perhaps she has been caught in a hunter's trap," said Crow. "He may even have killed her.

"We must go and look for our friend," said Tortoise. "Dear Crow, why don't you fly over the forest and see if you can find her?"

"Certainly," agreed Crow, "I shall go at once."

So the Crow flew over the forest, looking here and there for Deer. As he flew, he called out, "Where are you, Deer? Where are you?"

At last he heard a faint voice in reply. It was Deer.

"Help! I am here. Help me!"

"Oh, there you are, friend," said Crow. "I have been looking for you everywhere."

Crow flew down. He found Deer caught in a hunter's net.

"You are trapped," cried Crow. "What can I do to

help you? Shall I fly back to our friends for help?"

"Oh, please do," answered Deer with tears in her eyes. "Please do something quickly."

So Crow flew back to the lake. When the Tortoise and Mouse saw Crow coming, they shouted, "Have you found our friend? Have you found Deer?"

"Yes, yes, my friends, I have," replied Crow. "She is in great danger."

Crow then told them how he had found Deer trapped in a hunter's net.

Tortoise thought quickly. "Mouse can cut the net with his teeth and set our friend free," he said.

"Yes, yes, I can," said Mouse. "How shall I get there?"

"I can easily carry you on my back," said Crow.

"Come on, then, let us go," cried Mouse. And he jumped onto Crow's back.

Away Crow flew with Mouse on his back. They soon reached the place where Deer was.

The Mouse got off Crow's back and began to cut the net with his sharp teeth.

Soon Deer was free. She stood up and shook herself. By then Tortoise had reached there, crawling all the way.

"Oh, how nice to see you, Tortoise!" cried his friends.

For a while the four friends were busy talking about Deer's escape.

Suddenly they heard the sound of someone coming, through the forest. Was it the hunter?

At once Crow flew to the top of a tall tree.

Mouse hid himself in a hole.

Deer ran away.

Poor Tortoise, however, could not move quickly. Slowly he walked towards a big, green bush.

The hunter arrived and saw there was nothing under the net. "Oh, the deer has escaped!" he shouted.

Looking around, he saw a tortoise crawling towards the bush.

"Ha! A tortoise!" cried the hunter. "There will be something at least for my dinner."

He quickly grabbed the tortoise, put him in his bag and carried him off.

Crow, who was still at the top of the tree, saw what the hunter did.

"Oh, Mouse! Oh, Deer!" he called, "come quickly! Our friend Tortoise is now in danger."

At once, Mouse and Deer came running to the Crow, and he told them how the hunter had carried away the Tortoise in his bag.

"What can we do to set our friend free?" asked Crow.

"We must do something quickly," said Mouse, "before the hunter gets home."

"I know what to do," Deer said. "I shall go and stand in the path of the hunter, pretending to eat grass. As soon as he sees me, he will drop the bag and run after me. Mouse can then cut open the bag with his teeth, and Tortoise will be free."

"Supposing the hunter catches you?" asked Crow.

"Oh, don't worry about that," replied Deer. "I can run very fast."

So Deer stood in the path of the hunter, nibbling at the grass.

"A deer! A deer!" cried the hunter.

He dropped the bag and ran after Deer. The Mouse quickly cut open the bag, and Tortoise got out as fast as he could and hid under a bush.

The hunter could not catch the deer and soon stopped running after her. He came back to his bag.

"This tortoise is fairly fat," he said. "It will be enough for my dinner tonight."

When the hunter found his bag empty, he could not believe his eyes.

"What? No tortoise?" he cried. "How could he escape? How unlucky I am!"

"First the deer escaped from my net and now even this slow tortoise has got out of my bag. "Alas! there will be no dinner for me tonight!"

Tortoise, Mouse, Crow, and Deer quietly watched the hunter as he went away with the empty bag in his hand.

The Blue Jackal

ONCE A jackal was roaming about in search of food. It was an unlucky day for him. He could not get anything to eat.

Tired and hungry, he walked on and on until he strayed into a city.

He knew it was not safe for a jackal to walk about in a city. He was so hungry that he had to take the risk.

'I must find food,' he said to himself, 'but I hope I won't be attacked by men or dogs.'

Suddenly he heard dogs barking. He was afraid they would soon be after him.

He broke into a run. The dogs saw him and ran after him.

The jackal ran faster and faster to get away from the dogs who were close behind him.

In despair the jackal ran into a house. It belonged to a dyer. In the yard was a large tub filled with blue dye. The jackal fell into it.

The dogs could not find the jackal, so they went away.

The jackal stayed in the tub until he was sure the dogs had gone away. Then he crawled out.

He was surprised to find that he had become blue all over. He did not know what to do. So he hurried back to the jungle. All the animals who saw him ran away in fear. They had never seen an animal of that colour.

The jackal realized they were afraid of him. He was quick to think of a plan to take advantage of their fear.

"Why do you run away?" he cried. "Come back and listen to me."

The animals stopped running. They stood at a distance and looked at him. They were still afraid to go near him.

"Come, all of you," cried the jackal again. "Call your friends, too. I have something important to tell you."

One by one the animals went near the jackal. Tigers, elephants, monkeys, rabbits, deer, and many others. They stood around him.

"You need not be afraid of me," said the jackal. "You are safe. God has sent me here to be your king. I shall protect you."

The animals believed what he said.

"Your Majesty," they said, bowing low, "we accept you as our king. We thank God for sending you to us. Please tell us what to do."

"You are to look after your king well," said the jackal."You are to provide him with all the food he needs."

"Certainly, Your Majesty," the animals promised, "we shall do everything for our king's comfort. What more can we do for you?"

"You must always be loyal to your king," the jackal replied. "Then the king will protect you from your enemies."

The animals were satisfied. From then on, they sent the jackal all kinds of delicious food and looked after him well.

The jackal lived like a king. Every day the animals went to him with their problems. The king listened to them and told them what to do.

One day, as the king sat in his court, a noise was heard in the distance.

It was the howling of a pack of jackals.

He had not heard the voice of jackals for a long time. He felt happy and his eyes filled with tears of joy.

Forgetting he was king, the blue jackal raised his head and howled.

Immediately the animals knew who he really was—just a jackal! He had been cheating them all along.

They were so angry that they rushed at him to tear him to pieces.

The jackal was already on the run!

The Brahmin And The Goat

ONE DAY, a Brahmin received a goat as a gift. Carrying it on his shoulders, he set out for home.

Three rogues saw the Brahmin carrying the goat. They were hungry.

"That is a nice fat goat," said one of them.

"Yes," said another, "it will make a good meal for the three of us. How can we get the goat?"

"Listen," said the third rogue, "I have a plan."

He whispered into the ears of the other two.

They all laughed and hurried away.

A little later, one of the rogues came up to the Brahmin. "Holy sir," he said politely, "why are you carrying that dog on your shoulders? I am surprised to see a Brahmin carrying a dog."

"Dog?" shouted the Brahmin. "What are you talking about? Are you blind? This is a goat I have just received as a gift."

"Now don't be angry with me, sir," pleaded the

rogue. "I am only telling you what I see. I will say nothing more. Please pardon me, sir."

The rogue went away.

The Brahmin walked on, muttering angrily to himself.

A little further along the road, another of the rogues came up to him.

He looked at the goat, then at the Brahmin.

"Respected sir," he said in a sad voice, "you should not carry a dead calf. Is it not disgraceful for a calf? Is it not disgraceful for a Brahmin to carry a dead animal?"

"Dead calf? Dead animal?" shouted the Brahmin. "What nonsense are you talking? Are you blind? Don't you know a live goat when you see one? This is a gift I have just received."

"Please don't get angry with me, sir," replied the rogue.

"Carry a calf if you want, a live one or even a dead one. It does not matter to me one bit. I will say no more. Please yourself!"

On walked the Brahmin. Now he was a little worried. From time to time he glanced at the animal. It was a goat, all right!

Soon he met the third rogue. He shook his head and said, "Pardon me, but I must tell you, sir, that what you are doing is most improper."

"Improper?" asked the Brahmin. "What is improper?"

"It is not proper, sir, for a holy man to carry a donkey. A Brahmin should not even touch such an animal. You should know that. Put it down, sir, before anyone else sees what you are carrying."

The Brahmin was too puzzled to be angry. This was the third man he had met. And each had seen his goat as something different. First a dog, then a dead calf, and now a donkey!

Was this goat, then, a goblin or a demon? Could it change into something else every few minutes? Perhaps these men were right, after all.

Frightened, the Brahmin flung the goat down and ran home as fast as he could.

The rogue picked up the goat and hurried back to his friends. They were happy their plan had worked.

A Wise Old Bird

DEEP IN a forest stood a very tall tree. Its leafy branches spread out like strong arms.

This tree was the home of a flock of wild geese. They felt safe there.

One of the geese was a wise old bird.

He noticed a small creeper at the foot of the tree. He spoke to the other birds about it.

"Do you see that creeper?" he said to them. "Let us destroy it.

"Why must we destroy it?" asked the geese in surprise. "It is so small. What harm can it do?"

"My friends," replied the wise old bird, "that little creeper will soon grow. As it creeps up this tree, it will become thick and strong."

"What of that?" asked the geese. "What harm can a creeper do to us?"

"Don't you see?" replied the wise bird. "With the help of that creeper, it will be possible for someone to climb this tree. A hunter can come

up and kill us all. So, Let us destroy it."

"Well, there is no hurry," they replied. "The creeper is very small. It would be a pity to destroy it now."

"Destroy the creeper while it is still young," the old bird advised. "Now it is tender and you can cut it easily. Later it will become hard and you will not be able to cut it."

"We will see, we will see," answered the birds.

They did not destroy the creeper. They forgot the wise old bird's advice.

As the creeper grew, it began winding its way up the tree. Stronger and stronger it became, until it was as strong as a thick rope.

One morning, when the geese had gone out in search of food, a hunter came to the place.

'So this is where the wild geese live,' he said to himself. 'When they come back in the evening, I shall catch them.'

The hunter climbed up the tree with the help of the creeper. He got to the top and spread his net there. Then he climbed down and went away.

In the evening, the geese returned home. They did not notice the net. As they flew into the tree, they were trapped. They struggled hard to get out, but could not.

"Help! Help!" cried the geese. "We are caught in the hunter's net. Oh, what shall we do?"

"Don't make a fuss now," said the wise old bird. "Long ago I had told you to destroy the creeper, but you did not. Now see what has happened. Tomorrow morning the hunter will come back and kill us all."

"We were foolish," wept the birds. "We are

sorry we did not listen to you. Please tell us what to do?"

"Then listen carefully," replied the wise bird. "When the hunter comes, you must all pretend to be dead. Just lie still. The hunter will not harm dead birds. He will throw us to the ground. It will then be easy for him to climb down, collect the dead birds, and take them home. When the last of us has been thrown down, we must quickly get up and fly away."

In the morning, the hunter came to the tree and climbed up. He looked at the geese in the net.

'They are all dead,' he muttered to himself.

He threw them out of the net one by one.

The birds lay still until the last one had been thrown down. Then, all at once, they got up, flapped their wings, and flew away.

The hunter was taken by surprise. He stood staring after the geese.

"My father asked me to mend my ways," said the prince.

"That is what my father told me, too!" said the minister's son.

"And mine too," said the merchant's son. "He went on to add that he would turn me out of the house if I did not mend my ways!"

"This is too bad," said the prince. "We cannot put up with such insult even if it is from our father. Let us go away."

"How can we go away?" asked the minister's son. "We have no money of our own. We may have to get the money from our father."

"Let us find a way of making money," said the merchant's son. "There is a mountain not far from here. I'm told there are precious stones and gems at the top."

"If so, let us climb the mountain," said the prince. "If we find some precious stones, we will not have to depend on our father."

The three friends set out for the mountain. They crossed a wide river and passed through a dark forest.

Finally, they reached the mountain and climbed to the top. They were lucky, for each one of them found a gem of great value.

"Now we can go home," they said.

As they climbed down, they thought of the difficult journey ahead. They would have to pass through the dark forest again.

"The robbers and thieves in the forest," said the

merchant's son, "might kill us and take our gems away."

"That is true," agreed the prince. "We must think of a way of getting our gems safely home."

"I know what to do," said the minister's son. "We should swallow the gems before we enter the forest. We shall carry them safely in our stomachs."

"That is a good idea," agreed the prince. "No one will know they are there."

As they approached the forest, they sat down to eat. Each of them swallowed his gem with a mouthful of food.

It so happened that a thief had been following the three friends. He heard what they said and saw what they did.

He decided to kill the friends and get the gems for himself. When they were about to enter the forest, the thief went to them and said, "Good masters, ahead lies a dark forest. I am afraid of going through it alone. May I join you?"

The friends were glad to have one more in their party.

Half way through the forest was a village. The headman of the village had a parrot. He was fond of it and could understand all that it said. He believed that the parrot always spoke the truth.

The four men reached the village. As they passed the hut where the headman lived, the parrot spoke, "The travellers have gems!" he cried, "the travellers have gems!"

The headman heard the parrot. He wanted to get

the gems for himself. So he sent his men after the travellers. They were caught and brought back to the village.

The headman searched them but did not find any gems on them. 'My parrot must be wrong this time,' he thought. The travellers were set free.

As soon as they left the village the parrot spoke again. "The travellers have gems! The travellers have gems!"

'My parrot has never been wrong,' the headman said to himself. 'The travellers must have gems with them.'

Once more the thief and the three friends were caught and taken before the headman.

This time he made a thorough search. He even made them take off their clothes. Still he could not find the gems.

"My parrot always speaks the truth," he said. "The gems are nowhere to be seen. Perhaps you have swallowed them."

The thief and the friends kept quiet.

"I know what to do," the headman went on. "Tomorrow morning I shall cut open your stomachs. I shall get the gems all right!"

The headman locked them up in a room. None of the four was able to sleep. They were all frightened and could only think of the dreadful fate that awaited them in the morning.

The thief sat thinking. 'There is no gem in my stomach,' he said to himself. 'If I ask the headman

say: 'You, the king of the elephants, have brought your herd to my holy lake and soiled its waters. You have killed thousands of rabbits on your way to the lake. You know that rabbits are under my special protection. Everyone knows the king of the rabbits lives with me. I ask you not to kill anymore rabbits. Otherwise something terrible will happen to you and your herd'."

The king of the elephants was shocked. He looked at the little rabbit.

"You are right," he said. "We may have killed many rabbits on our way to the lake. I shall see that you do not suffer anymore. I shall request the Moon to forgive me for my sins. Please tell me what I should do."

"Come with me, alone," replied the rabbit. "Come, I shall take you to the Moon."

The little rabbit took the huge elephant to the lake. There they saw the Moon reflected in the still waters.

"There, Your Majesty, meet the Moon," said the little rabbit.

"Let me worship the divine Moon," said the elephant, and dipped his trunk into the water.

At once the water was disturbed. The Moon seemed to move to and fro.

The rabbit said, "Now the Moon is angrier than ever."

"Why?" asked the king. "What have I done?"

"You have touched the holy waters of the lake," replied the rabbit.

"Where can we get a camel?" he asked.

"There is a desert some miles away. I have just been flying over it. I saw a lone camel there. It looked big and fat."

The lion looked at his other advisers. They were wise, experienced. He wanted their opinion. The fox and the leopard did not know much about a desert. Yet they did not want the crow to seem wiser. So they said it was a good idea. The crow could fly ahead and show them the way.

Next morning, the lion and his aides set off for the desert. They soon reached the edge of the desert. Once they had left the shelter of the forest, the blazing sun beat down on them. It was unbearably hot.

High up in the cool air, the crow flew.

"Hurry along," he called out. "The camel is not far off." The lion could go no further. The hot sand had burned his paws.

"Stop!" he shouted to the others. "Let us go back to the forest. I do not care for camel meat."

His advisers were frightened. The forest was far behind them. They did not know how to get the lion back home. The leopard wanted to run away.

The crow wanted to wait and watch.

The clever fox thought of a plan. Off he ran into the desert, saying, "I will bring some help." After some time, he found the camel.

How surprised the camel was to see a fox in the desert!

"Hurry up," said the fox. "Our king wants you at once."

"Our king? Who is that? I don't know any king. I know only my master for whom I carry loads across the desert."

"Our king is a lion. He has killed your master. You are now free. The lion invites you to live at his court. Come along." So the camel followed the fox.

When the fox and the camel reached the lion's camp, the crow and the leopard were surprised. Even the lion was pleased, in spite of his burned paws.

The camel was presented to the king.

"Get on the camel's back, Your Majesty," said the fox. "We will return home."

The lion at once jumped on to the camel's back. The fox and the leopard sat behind him. With the

crow flying ahead as the guide, they set off on the long journey back.

By the time they returned to the forest, they were tired and hungry.

The fox, the leopard, and the crow looked at the camel. They looked at each other and smiled. They had brought the camel along for the king. Now it was time for dinner.

The lion knew what his courtiers were thinking. He turned to the camel. "Friend," he said, "I have to thank you for saving my life. You are welcome to live with us as long as you like. I promise you protection."

The courtiers were shocked. Had they not risked their lives to get him camel meat? And now the king wanted to let the camel live.

How could they say anything? After all he was their king.

The lion's paws were so badly burned that he could not hunt. He was very hungry indeed.

"Fox! Leopard! Crow!" he roared, "don't you see I am ill and hungry? Go and get me some food!"

The courtiers had to obey the king. So they went, but not far. They sat down to discuss what to do.

"I know," said the fox after a while, "we shall make the camel request the lion to eat him."

He told the others of his plan. They agreed it was a good idea.

Back they went to the king.

First the crow stepped forward, bowing low. "Your Majesty, we have found no food. But we cannot let you suffer. I am a little creature. Please eat me."

The fox pushed the crow aside. "I have more flesh on me. Please eat me, Sire."

The leopard rushed in. "I am even bigger, Your Majesty."

The camel felt he should not be found wanting in loyalty to his king.

"Your Majesty," he said, "I, too, am willing to sacrifice my life to save yours. These friends are more useful to you than I am. Eat me instead."

At these words the crow, the fox, and the leopard got ready to pounce on the camel.

The lion stopped them. “You are all good and loyal subjects. I am touched by your offers. I accept them all. I shall eat you one by one, in the order in which you offered yourselves.”

There was not a moment to lose.

Away flew the crow. Away ran the fox and the leopard.

The lion had a hearty laugh. Then he turned to the camel. “You have been loyal and good. You shall be my friend as long as I live.”

The camel was grateful and happy.

The lion said to himself:

‘To be a king is good,
To be kind is better.’

Three Fish

THERE LIVED three big fish in a lake. They were close friends, but quite unlike one another.

One of them was wise. Whatever he did was after careful thought.

Another was intelligent and resourceful. For any problem he had, he would use his brains and find a solution. He was ever cheerful.

The third fish believed in fate. Whatever was to happen would happen, and nobody could stop it.

One day, the wise fish was leaping about in the water. He heard a fisherman telling another, "What a fine one that is, and big, too. This lake is full of good fish. Let us fish here tomorrow."

On hearing this, the fish rushed to his friends. "Let us leave this lake. This canal here will take us to another lake."

"I don't think I will leave this place," said the resourceful fish. "If the fishermen come, I shall find some way of saving myself."

The third one said, "I have been here since I was born. Why should I leave the place of my birth? Whatever will be, will be."

The wise fish did not want to take any risk. He left the lake by the canal and went to another.

The fishermen came the next morning and cast their net. The two friends who had not left the lake were caught in it, along with many other fish.

The resourceful one immediately thought of a way out. He pretended to be dead. The fishermen threw him out with the other dead fish. He managed to crawl to the edge of the lake and jump in.

The fish who believed in fate kept jumping up and down in the net. One of the fishermen struck him dead.

The Cave That Talked

A HUNGRY lion roamed the forest in search of food. He could not find any animal to kill. The more he wandered, the hungrier he became. Finally, he saw the mouth of a big cave.

The lion said to himself, 'I think some animal lives here. I shall wait behind the bush opposite, until he comes out. I shall pounce on him.'

He waited for a long time, but no one came out:

The lion thought, 'The fellow must have gone out. I shall go in and wait for him. I am sure he will just walk in and into my mouth.'

So the lion went in and hid himself in a dark corner.

The cave was the home of the jackal. He returned shortly. As he was about to enter the cave, he noticed footprints. 'These are the footprints of a big animal. Probably he is still inside. It may be dangerous to go in. Let me find out,' he said to himself.

The jackal was clever. He called out in a loud voice, "Hello, dear cave! My dear cave."

There was silence. He shouted again, "Hello, cave! Hello, my dear cave! Why don't you answer me? Are you dead? What has happened to you? You always welcome me when I return home. Why are you quiet today? If you do not reply, I shall go to some other cave."

The lion heard the shouts of the jackal. He said to himself, 'This cave is in the habit of welcoming the jackal. Now it is afraid of me and does not talk. The jackal will go away if he is not welcomed.'

So the lion roared, "Hello, hello! Welcome home, my friend."

'He must be hungry indeed,' mused the wise jackal as he fled the place.

The Elephants And The Mice

THERE WAS a large and beautiful city beside a lake. It had many temples and fine houses. The people who lived there were happy and prosperous.

With the passage of time, the city lay in ruins.

The people had fled, taking with them their cows and bullocks, horses and elephants.

Only the mice in the city stayed on. They moved into the houses and temples. It became a city of mice.

Soon there were more mice than ever—generations of them. Great-generations and grandparents, fathers and mothers, husbands and wives, uncles and aunts, brothers and sisters, and lots and lots of baby mice.

All of them lived happily together. Almost every day there was some celebration or the other. There were spring and harvest festivals, weddings, and other get-togethers.

In a jungle far away from this city of mice, lived some elephants.

They were a large herd and their king was a big tusker. Noble and kind, he ruled his herd well. The elephants loved him. The tusker and his herd were happy in the jungle, until a great disaster befell them. There was no rain for several years and all the rivers and tanks dried up. They had no water to drink.

Far and wide, the elephants went in search of water. One of them reported to the king that he had seen a city in ruins. On the other side of it was a lake.

The king was delighted. He led his herd to the lake.

On the way, they had to pass through the city of mice. As the thirsty elephants hurried along, they did not notice that thousands of mice were being trampled to death. Thousands more were injured.

Mice doctors and nurses did all they could to help the dying and the injured. As more and more elephants rushed through the city, more and more mice were killed and injured. Such a terrible calamity had never befallen the mice before. What could they do?

How were they to stop the elephants from destroying them? The mice got together to consider the best course of action. A wise old mouse suggested they go to the king of the elephants and plead with him. He might agree to stop his herd from passing through their city again.

All the mice thought it was a good, practical idea. They chose three mice to speak for them.

The three went to the king of the elephants, bowed low, and said, "Your Majesty, you are big and powerful. Perhaps you are not aware of the great harm done when your herd passes through our city. We are small and get crushed under your feet. Many thousands of us have already been killed and many more injured.

"We fear that if you pass through the city again, none of us will be left alive. So, we have come to request you to return to your jungle by some other way. If you do that, we shall always be grateful to you and be your friends. We admit, we are small, but some day we may be able to help you.

The tusker was moved.

"You are right," he told them. "Now, go and live in peace. I will see that you do not suffer anymore."

Years later, the king of a nearby country wanted many elephants for his army.

He sent out his men to capture as many as they could.

They came to the jungle where the tusker and his herd lived. They were happy to find so many elephants.

The men dug deep pits and covered them with twigs and leaves. These were traps for elephants.

The king of the elephants and many of his herd fell into the pits. They tried hard to get out, but could not.

The men came back, bringing with them some tame elephants. With strong ropes, they pulled the trapped elephants out of the pits and tied them firmly.

The men went back with the tame elephants to report to their king.

The captive elephants were in a sad plight. Their king was distressed to find that so many of his herd had been caught along with him. How could they escape? He could not think of a way out.

It was then that he remembered the mice in the city. They had said they would help.

The tusker called his queen. She had not been trapped.

He asked her to rush to the city of mice and tell them what had happened.

The queen hastened to the mice. They were sorry to hear that the elephants were in such peril. "We will certainly do our best to help our friends," they assured her.

Thousands of mice rushed to the place where the elephants were.

With their sharp teeth, they cut through the thick ropes and finally set the elephants free.

There was great rejoicing all round. The mice were happy they were able to repay a debt.

One of them clambered up the trunk of the king. “We are friends,” he said. “You were kind to us once. Now we are glad we could be of help.”

The mice and the elephants got together to celebrate.

“This is the happiest festival of all,” they joyfully sang in chorus. “It is indeed a festival of friendship between mice and elephants.”